Mum and Gran went on <u>holiday</u>.
They went to Scotland.
They took the <u>children</u>.

1

They stayed in a cottage.
The cottage was by a lake.
It had a boat.

'I like it here,' said Biff.
'We can go sailing.'
'And fishing,' said Kipper.

Everyone had a good time.
Biff and Kipper went fishing.

Gran and Chip painted a picture.
Mum sat in the sun and read a book.
'This is fun,' she said.

Everyone looked at Gran's picture.
'Oh Gran!' said Chip.
She had painted a monster.

Kipper looked at the monster.
Gran laughed.
'There's no such thing,' she said.

Mum went shopping.
She took Kipper.
Biff and Chip stayed with Gran.

8

Mum looked at the shops.
'Let's get Dad a postcard,' she said.

Kipper went into a shop.
'I want a monster for me and
a postcard for Dad,' he said.

Kipper posted the card to Dad.
'I wish Dad was here,' he said.

Gran wanted to play a joke on Mum.
'Let's make a monster,' she said.

'I don't get it,' said Biff.
'Wait and see,' said Gran.

They put the monster in the lake.
It made the children laugh.
'It looks brilliant!' said Chip.

14

'What a good joke,' said Biff.
'What a good joke to play on Mum.'

Mum and Kipper came back.
Gran pulled the rope.
The monster went across the lake.

16

'A real monster,' said Kipper.
'I don't believe it,' said Mum.
'There's no such thing.'

Some people saw Gran's monster.
They were amazed.
They took photographs.

The children watched television.
'Gran's monster!' said Chip.
'Oh no!' groaned Biff.

The next day lots of people came.
There were lots and lots and
    lots of people.

They wanted to see the monster.
'Oh Gran!' said Mum.
'Now look what you've done.'

Gran told everyone about
    the monster.
'It was just a joke,' she said.

A man from the television came.
Mum was cross with Gran but
everyone laughed.

Gran was sorry.
'A monster?' she said.
'There is no such thing.'